The Vikings in Ireland

This story was adapted by author Ann Carroll
and illustrated by Derry Dillon

Published 2015
Poolbeg Press Ltd

123 Grange Hill, Baldoyle
Dublin 13, Ireland

Text © Poolbeg Press Ltd 2015

A catalogue record for this book is available from the British Library.

ISBN 978 1 78199 928 8

Cover design and illustrations by Derry Dillon
Printed by GPS Colour Graphics Ltd, Alexander Road, Belfast BT6 9HP

This book belongs to

- -

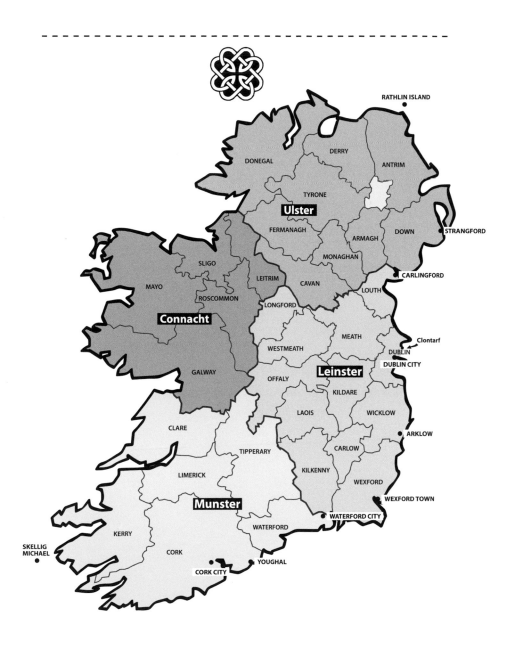

Also in the Nutshell series

The Arrival of the Vikings

On the east coast of Ireland one bright morning in the year 795, a number of longboats skimmed onto the shore. No one in the settlement spotted them. The rowers silently downed their oars and stared across the dunes, studying the church and monastery and the outlying houses.

Smoke curled above the roofs. In the fields farmers tended to cattle or crops. Women chatted as they spread laundry to dry or collected water for cooking, while children played nearby.

In the monastery the monks were busy. Among them were artists and craftsmen: scribes creating great manuscripts with delicate lettering in beautiful colours, goldsmiths making chalices and crucifixes, stonemasons carving figures and patterns on a Celtic Cross.

The men on the shore made no sound until their leader raised his sword and shouted, "Odin, God of Battle, give us strength!"

The fierce, bearded warriors waved their weapons and stormed the settlement.

Terror!

They plundered the church and monastery, destroyed the manuscripts, robbed the treasures and herded together monks, farmers, women and children.

Swiftly the leader picked his prisoners: strong youths, young females, children old enough to follow orders. These would be slaves. The rest were killed.

But, unknown to them, the raiders left one witness behind.

The Boy Who Escaped

Before the mayhem started ten-year-old Malachy, an apprentice scribe, had been practising the letter M, trying to get the right flourish and thickness with his quill.

Brother Anselm was very grumpy. "Wretched work!" he told his pupil. "You'll never make a scribe at this rate."

When screams shattered the air, the monk strode to the window. Then he turned to Malachy. "Listen! Don't ask questions. Get into that cupboard and stay absolutely silent. Now!"

He pushed the boy into the small cupboard and was back standing by the table when three raiders thundered in. Swiftly one clouted the monk across the head while the other two shoved and kicked him out the door. The boy could see through a small gap and was terrified.

But no one thought to look in the cupboard.

Malachy's Account

As soon as it was safe, Malachy fled the scene and didn't stop till he arrived at the next settlement, ten miles away. There he told his story to the Abbot.

"When they took Brother Anselm away, I went to the window and peeped out. The women and children were wailing and crying. The strangers had axes and swords. First they killed the older men, then anyone else they didn't want, including all the infants. I never heard such sorrow. "

"Were there survivors?"

"Yes. They lined them up and marched them down to the shore, not caring about their suffering. I sneaked after and hid behind the dunes. They had long, narrow boats on the shore. These they pushed into the sea, packed on their prisoners and plunder, then rowed away, hoisting their sails as they went."

"I've heard of these raiders. They are Vikings from the north – 'Norsemen' – from Norway, Sweden and Denmark."

"Vikings?" Malachy had never heard the term.

"That's what they call themselves. It must mean 'pirates'. Earlier this year they attacked the islands from Rathlin down to Skellig Michael. Now they've turned on the mainland. How many did they kill?"

"I didn't stay to count. It was a nightmare and I ran away."

"There was nothing you could do. Next time we'll be prepared."

The Perfect Plan

But for many years afterwards the Norsemen continued their raids along the east coast and no one was able for them.

They were fierce and strong and chose the best warriors as leaders. The longboats were fast and travelled a great distance. Their weapons were huge axes and double-edged swords.

So they probably had the best boats and the best weapons in the world right then.

They also had a six-point plan which worked perfectly:

1. *Arrive unexpectedly.*
2. *Swoop quickly and violently so that people are overcome with fear.*
3. *Rob the monasteries and the churches of their treasures.*
4. *Take the young and the fit as prisoners.*
5. *Kill the rest.*
6. *Cause the utmost terror so that the word 'Viking' is dreaded throughout the land.*

Settling Down

But in the 9th century, many Vikings began to want a different life.

One such warrior was Eric Svenson. By the time he was twenty-eight he'd spent ten years as a raider and wanted to settle down, marry and have a family.

His leader, Olaf, was of the same mind. "Dublin would be a good place, Eric."

"Dublin?"

"A settlement on the River Liffey – a Viking settlement where we're building houses and trading."

"And will we have peace?"

His leader laughed. "Peace is impossible," he said. "The Irish hate us. Dublin is often attacked, so we'll still be fighting. And we'll be expected to go on raids and increase Viking wealth. But at least we'll have a home."

So Eric settled in Dublin which was fast becoming a town. He had a long wooden house built, with a central hearth for cooking, and furnished it with a fine table, and wide benches which doubled as beds.

There was an outside bath house and toilet (toilet paper didn't exist so sheep's wool was used).

Everything he needed – knives, spoons, plates, candles, bedclothes – he bought from craftsmen.

When it was all finished, he sighed, "There's no point to any of this without a wife!"

But there wasn't a suitable Viking woman he could marry in the settlement at the time and there was a shortage of slave girls for sale, so Eric made a plan: "I'll take part in the next raid, capture a beautiful girl and she'll be my wife. Simple!"

An Irish Victory

By now Malachy was a middle-aged monk and he'd never forgotten the violent raid when he was a ten-year-old. Over the years he had often pondered the Viking problem.

"We must build a round tower," he decided, "and always have a lookout at the highest window, who can warn us in time! We can store our treasures and our weapons there."

So the tower was built and, when Eric's raiding party came, the lookout rang a large bell with great vigour.

At once the monks made for the ladder at the bottom of the tower, climbed in through the first small doorway and drew the ladder up after them. They threw rocks and fired arrows at the raiders below.

Surprised, the Vikings turned to the houses and outbuildings, but here too the menfolk put up a valiant fight. They were farmers, not warriors, but they were determined to do battle.

Eric made his way into one of the houses and found a teenage girl, Emer, trying to hide behind a barrel. Emer's mother was long dead and her father was away buying cattle.

Eric thought she was very beautiful. "Freya, Goddess of Love and Beauty, has rewarded me," he said.

Life in Dublin

Eric managed to capture the girl. He was the only happy Viking that day. Many had been killed. Few prisoners and no treasure had been taken. To cap it all, Thor, God of Thunder, let loose a terrible storm as they headed home.

He settled down with Emer, who in time grew fond enough of her husband, for he made sure to treat her well, even sending a messenger to tell her father how she was faring.

Over the years the fighting lessened, then ceased. The raiders stopped coming from the north.

Eric became a trader, buying and selling goods to other Viking towns and life was good.

Sven

Emer and Eric had one son, Sven, who loved hearing the sagas about Viking heroes and especially how his father had been a great warrior.

In Sven's lifetime, all along the east coast of
Ireland, Viking towns prospered – Carlingford,
Dublin, Waterford, Cork and Youghal. Mid-century
the raids on Ireland stopped and Dublin became
a town of rich merchants.

Sven too became a trader. He travelled on business throughout Europe and became a wealthy man.

So when his father died, Sven gave him a Viking funeral, fit for a hero. The body was placed in the middle of a longboat, alongside his best possessions including his weapons.

They sacrificed some animals and people and laid them beside him, because they believed that their spirits would accompany him to the next world. The boat was then buried and a big mound of earth and stones was piled on top to mark the place.

New Invasions

Malachy, Eric and even Sven were long dead when the raids from the north began again. In 921 the Norsemen founded Wexford and then Limerick a year later. By now Viking power had spread to Britain, the Isle of Man and Orkney, to parts of Europe and even to Iceland, Greenland and Russia. Increasingly the Irish became more and more fed up. No matter how bravely they fought, they failed to conquer the enemy.

Then, in the second half of the 10th century, came a great Irish leader.

Brian Boru

Brian Boru was a Munster man who, over the years, defeated the Vikings in Cashel and Limerick and then, best of all, beat Sitric, who ruled Dublin. Eventually Brian became High King of Ireland.

But he had one great Irish enemy, Mael Morda, who envied him his power and joined forces with Sitric.

They knew their enemy was powerful. "We do not have enough men to defeat Brian," Mael Morda told his ally.

"I have friends among the Vikings on Orkney and the Isle of Man," said Sitric. "And there's nothing they love more than a great battle!"

The Battle of Clontarf

And so it was that Sigurd of Orkney and Brodir from the Isle of Man came with their armies. They joined Sitric and Mael Morda at Clontarf on Palm Sunday 1014.

Brian marched to meet them and on Good Friday the battle began.

The High King fought bravely but he was seventy-three years old and had to take a rest now and again in his tent. He used the time to pray and during one break, while he was on his knees, Brodir the Viking sneaked into the tent and killed him.

Fury made Brian's men fight on ferociously and they won, killing most of the enemy.

This was the decisive battle against the Vikings. Never again would they have the same power in Ireland.

In time they intermarried with the native people, stopped fighting and became Irish: friends not enemies.

The Viking Legacy in Ireland

They left behind place names such as Arklow, Wexford, Waterford, Strangford.

Some days of the week are called after their gods: Wednesday comes from Odin, God of War, who was also known as Woden, Thursday from Thor, God of Thunder, and Friday from Freya, Goddess of Beauty.

There are many Viking surnames in Ireland, for example Broderick. And anyone called MacAuliffe or MacManus belongs to the Viking clans of Olaf and Magnus.

They left a tradition of storytelling with their heroic tales or sagas.

They had their own letters, called runes, which were very different to our alphabet.

The Vikings were horrible in many ways, but also they were brave and clever. Great adventurers, they sought out the unknown.

For good or bad, they're part of our ancestry.

The End

Runes Alphabet

Elder Futhark

This is the earliest runic alphabet
(2nd to 8th centuries)

f	u	th	a	r	c/ch	g'	w	h

n	i	j	ei	p	x	s	t	b

e	m	l	ng	oe	d	a'	y

ea	io	k	g"	g	st

Runes Alphabet
Younger Futhark
(Also called the Scandinavian Futhark)

The Vikings used this version which has less runes

(9th to 11th centuries)

ᚠ	ᚢ	ᚦ	ᚬ
f	u	th	o
ᚱ	ᚴ	ᚼ	ᚾ
r	k	h	n
ᛁ	ᛅ	ᛋ	ᛏ
i	a	s	t
ᛒ	ᛘ	ᛚ	ᛦ
b	m	l	r(y)

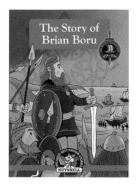

If you want to know more about Brian Boru, read Nutshell Number 9...

The Story of Brian Boru

If you enjoyed this book from
Poolbeg why not visit our website:

www.poolbeg.com

and get another book delivered straight
to your home or to a friend's home.

All books despatched within 24 hours.

POOLBEG

Why not join our mailing list
at www.poolbeg.com and get some
fantastic offers, competitions,
author interviews and much more?

@PoolbegBooks